Scavenger Guides

WASHINGTON, DC

AN INTERACTIVE TRAVEL GUIDE FOR KIDS

Also available

Scavenger Guides Chicago

Scavenger Guides New York City

Scavenger Guides

WASHINGTON, DC

AN INTERACTIVE TRAVEL GUIDE FOR KIDS

Daniel Ireland

Three Leaf Press
www.threeleafpress.com

Front cover photography: The White House in Washington, DC © Vacclav - Fotolia.com.

Back cover photography: Lincoln Memorial courtesy of Morgue File, morguefile.com: Michael J. Connors.

Photos courtesy of and copyright Free Range Stock, freerangestock.com: Chance Agrella 6, 17, 40; Dwight Tracy 34.

Photos courtesy of Morgue File, morguefile.com: Daniel T. Yara 10, 71; Kevin Connors 13, 39; Michelle Kwajafa 18, 23; Mary R. Vogt 57; Pindi Yath 67; Kenn W. Kiser 68.

Photos courtesy of Library of Congress Prints and Photographs Division, Washington, DC: 48.

Photos published under Creative Commons Attribution 2.0 Generic: Bernt Rostad 2; Amanda Spak 7; Selena Beckman-Harned 26; Ngoc Nguyen 28; Anna Levinzon 51; Herry Lawford 62; Michael Myers 72. Photos published under Creative Commons Attribution-ShareAlike 2.0 Generic: Jacob Fincher 3; Art Bromage 9; Rob Shenk 14; Andrew Hayward 42; Mack Male 52; Alex1961 58; Jeff Kubina 60.

All other photos by author unless otherwise noted.

The authors, publishers, and distributors of this book assume no responsibility for any injury, misadventure, or loss occurring from use of the information contained herein.

Published by Three Leaf Press
www.threeleafpress.com

Printed in the United States of America

First edition
ISBN: 978-0-9845866-1-5

CONTENTS

SCAVENGER ADVENTURE PLEDGE

I pledge to discover the natural, historical, and cultural beauty of the places I visit, to preserve them by respecting all local rules and customs, and to share my knowledge and experiences with others.

_____

(print name here)

A NOTE TO PARENTS

Many parents have reservations about traveling with children, but travel doesn't have to end when you start a family. Travel is a wonderful time for children to learn and grow - no matter their age. It is also a wonderful time to grow as a family.

Traveling as a family is an incredible experience! Your child will grow in their knowledge and understanding of the world in which they live, and you'll see the world in a whole new way - through the uninhibited eyes of your child. Embrace traveling with your children, and you may find that your kids are capable of much more than you imagined!

This travel guide is for children visiting Washington, DC and their parents. It is designed to engage your child in their travels and enhance their observational skills. Presented as a scavenger hunt, this interactive travel challenge will also help parents capture those teachable moments while traveling. This guide contains many interesting facts and useful pieces of information to help your child learn about Washington, DC, but its most important role is as a tool to jump-start dialogue between you and your child.

This book is not a comprehensive travel guide to Washington, DC. Most children would rather experience the sights and sounds of a region first-hand than read about them in the pages of a travel book. There are numerous guides available on how to get to Washington, DC, where to stay, where to eat, and what to see and do, but they are written for adults. Use those guides to plan your trip. Cross-reference the places you plan to visit with the locations presented in this Scavenger Guide, and you will be well-prepared for a more in-depth travel experience with your child.

Each section of this guide presents several "clues" that challenge your child to find certain locations, identify items, or complete experiences throughout Washington, DC. Each completed item earns 10 points. At the end of their travels, children add up their points and collect their award certificate. For some children, the challenge of the hunt is motivation enough. As a parent, you may wish to attach an additional reward, such as money for a souvenir or the opportunity for the child to choose where the family dines their last night of vacation. You know your child best. Be creative. Above all, have fun and enjoy this truly unique travel experience with your child!

Family travel can be both fun and informative.

Have a wonderful trip!

WHERE IS WASHINGTON, DC?

Washington, DC is located on the East Coast of the United States between the states of Maryland and Virginia. It is the capital city and center of government of the United States.

Washington, DC

A SCAVENGER ADVENTURE

Are you ready for an adventure? You've come to the right place! There is a lot to see and do in Washington, DC. This scavenger hunt will help you get the most out of your experience. Can you complete each item and become a Scavenger Guides World Explorer?

Welcome to your Scavenger Hunt Adventure around Washington, DC! You'll need to use your eyes and your brain to solve these challenges. Your scavenger hunt will take you to many of the most popular and famous museums, monuments, and other places of interest that make Washington, DC such an exciting place to visit. Whether you like history, art, science and technology, or just experiencing new places, you'll find plenty to do in the nation's capital.

Have fun on your hunt and good luck. You will have an absolutely wonderful time exploring this great city!

HOW IT WORKS

Your Scavenger Hunt Adventure has many challenges for you to complete during your visit to Washington, DC. You do not have to answer the challenges in order. Feel free to skip around as you visit various locations around the city. Also, don't feel you need to complete all the challenges in one day! Washington, DC is a big city, and it will take a lot of time and effort to complete your Scavenger Hunt Adventure. Correctly complete as many of the challenges on your scavenger hunt as you can. Keep track of each task you complete, then add up your points to win!

BEFORE YOU BEGIN

Read all the questions in your Scavenger Hunt Adventure before you start. This will help you get familiar with all the different challenges you will be asked to complete at a specific location. This will also help you use your time more

▲ The Lincoln Memorial and Reflecting Pool.

Many of the monuments and landmarks in Washington, DC commemorate important chapters in American history.

efficiently and minimize repeated visits to the same site.

Helpful Hints

Here are some suggestions to help you in your search:

✔ Read each scavenger hunt question carefully before you begin.

✔ Questions have been grouped by topic. Mark the questions that go with the areas you plan to visit each day. Do this each morning as you plan your day.

✔ Look carefully all around you before you record your answers. Sometimes a second search will reveal things missed at first glance.

✔ Ask the staff at a museum or site's information desk. They can often point you in the right direction.

✔ Check out a site's map for clues.

✔ Question a guard or police officer.

▲ **Korean War Veterans Memorial.**

The National Mall is the heart of Washington, DC and of the United States of America, honoring its commitment to democracy.

✔ Read signs and plaques carefully. They often reveal clues that will lead you to the answer.

✔ Check to see if the site has a computer information system for visitors to use.

✔ Look in gift shops. The postcards and books there often cover the site's main points of interest.

✔ Don't be afraid to ask your parents and siblings for help! They might see something you have missed.

WHEN YOU FINISH

After you have completed as many challenges as you can, add up all the points from the challenges you solved. There is a handy worksheet at the end of the scavenger hunt to help you with this task. Compare your total score with the award chart at the bottom of the worksheet and collect your Scavenger Guides Certificate.

Can you reach the level of World Explorer? Have fun on your adventure!

WELCOME TO WASHINGTON, DC

Washington, DC is the capital of the United States. It is located in the mid-Atlantic region on the east coast of the United States. Washington, DC is not a state, but rather a unique "federal district" created to serve as the nation's permanent capital.

Washington, DC is the center of U.S. government, but it is also a major cultural center and tourist destination. Washington, DC is especially popular with families. Here are our picks for the Top 10 Things for Kids in Washington, DC!

TOP 10 WASHINGTON, DC ATTRACTIONS

#10 National Museum of American History

What do Kermit the Frog and Abraham Lincoln's hat have in common? You can find both in the National Museum of American History! With a collection of more than 3 million artifacts of American history and culture, the museum is a great place for kids of all ages to learn about the nation's past. Look for touch stations throughout the museum for chances to interact with history.

#9 Smithsonian Discovery Rooms

Get a hands-on, behind-the scenes look at the Smithsonian museums as you explore a variety of games, puzzles, and scientific challenges in these family activity rooms. Hunt for animals in an African baobab tree at the National Museum of

▲ **United States Supreme Court Building.**

Visit the American History Museum's Spark!Lab to play games, conduct science experiments, and try your hand at inventing!

Natural History. Visit the Spark!Lab at the American History Museum to learn about inventors and their work. Join a design team at the Learning Lab in the National Air and Space Museum. Learning has never been so much fun!

#8 Three Branches of Government

The United States government is a democratic system based on the separation of powers among the executive (the presidency), the legislature (the two houses of Congress), and the judiciary (the federal courts). By visiting the White

House, the U.S. Capitol Building, and the U.S. Supreme Court, and exploring the roles of each branch, you can gain a better understanding of how this form of democratic government works.

#7 Museum of Natural History

The National Museum of Natural History is one of the most visited Smithsonian museums, and it's not hard to see why! Many of the exhibits offer hands-on and immersive experiences. The museum features a 3D IMAX theater and many interactive exhibits, including the Insect Zoo where you can touch and hold live insects and watch a tarantula feeding demonstration. You can even become an anthropologist and analyze real human bones in the Forensic Lab.

#6 Smithsonian's Discovery Theater

The Smithsonian's Discovery Theater

▲ National Museum of Natural History.

The Smithsonian Institution is the world's largest museum complex and research organization with 19 museums, 9 research centers, and the National Zoo.

is located in the Ripley Center on the National Mall. This live theater showcases classic stories and folktales for children of all ages. Many performances are interactive and are presented in a variety of formats, including puppet shows, storytelling, music, dance, and original plays.

#5 Bureau of Engraving & Printing

Watch real money being printed! Millions of dollars are printed, stacked, and cut each day at the Bureau of Engraving and Printing. Take a tour of the process from

▲ **Family fun at the National Zoo.**

design through final inspection. See what steps are taken to deter counterfeiters. The Bureau also prints White House invitations, cards, certificates, and other special security documents. But don't look for coins - those are produced at the United States Mint.

The Bureau of Engraving and Printing produces over $500 million in U.S. currency every day!

#4 National Zoo

This 163-acre zoological park in the heart of Washington, DC is a kid-favorite. The National Zoo is home to more than 400 different species of animals. The zoo's most famous residents are the giant pandas on loan from China, but other favorites include the gorillas and orangutans in the Ape House and the endangered Asian elephants. Step into the barn at the Kids' Farm to learn about alpacas, cows, donkeys, hogs, and goats. Then jump into the Pizza Garden with its twenty-two-foot-wide rubber pizza, complete with toppings,

Attend an animal training, feeding demonstration, or zoo keeper talk to learn more about the zoo and the animals that live there.

▲ **Washington Monument mirrored in the Reflecting Pool.**

that children can climb on.

#3 Washington Monument

Built in honor of George Washington, the nation's first president, the Washington Monument stands tall at the center of the National Mall. At just over 555 feet tall, the white obelisk is the tallest structure in Washington, DC. An elevator takes you to the top of the monument for a spectacular bird's eye view of the city and a unique perspective of the many monuments and historical buildings in the city, including the U.S. Capitol, the Lincoln Memorial, the White House, and the Jefferson Memorial.

#2 Lincoln Memorial

The Lincoln Memorial pays tribute to the 16th President of the United States, Abraham Lincoln, who fought to preserve the nation during the Civil War. Climb the many steps to the top of the memorial to view the large seated sculpture of Abraham Lincoln and read the carved inscriptions from two of his well-known speeches. Completed in 1922, the Lincoln Memorial has become a symbol of civil rights, justice, and democracy. Many notable events in history have occurred here, which you can learn about in the Legacy of Lincoln Museum located in the basement of the memorial.

#1 National Air and Space Museum

The National Air and Space museum

▲ Explore the history of space flight at the National Air and Space Museum.

Touch an actual Moon rock from the Apollo 17 manned mission to the Moon in the Milestones of Flight exhibit!

houses the largest collection of air and spacecraft in the world. Some of the historic aircraft on display include Orville and Wilbur Wright's 1903 Wright Flyer, Charles Lindbergh's *Spirit of St. Louis*, and the Apollo 11 Command Module. It's a great place to learn about the history and science of aviation and space flight. And there's plenty to do besides look! Climb aboard a real space station. Fly the Interactive Flight Simulator. Discover the four basic principles of flight and build a working model in the Learning Lab. With an IMAX theater and planetarium, this museum is a favorite with kids and adults!

DISCOVER WASHINGTON, DC

Whatever you decide to do, Washington, DC is an exciting city to visit! Have fun, and don't forget to record your thoughts and observations in your daily journal at the back of this guide.

Ready to explore? Let's go on a Washington, DC Scavenger Hunt Adventure!

3 | CAPITOL HILL HUNT

When people think of Washington, DC, they often think of the famous dome of the U.S. Capitol. For many, it is the symbol of democracy. The Capitol Building is where senators and representatives from all fifty states meet to make laws. The Capitol also marks the center of the city. Near the Capitol Building, you'll find many other government buildings, including the Library of Congress, with the world's largest collection of books, and the U.S. Supreme Court, the nation's highest judicial court. Capitol Hill is an area bustling with activity.

UNITED STATES CAPITOL

The United States Capitol sits atop Capitol Hill at the eastern end of the National Mall. It has been the center of the United States legislature for over 200 years. The cornerstone was laid by George Washington in 1793. It is the meeting place of the United States Congress - the Senate and the House of Representatives.

1 Find a famous civil war general sitting astride his favorite horse, Cincinnatus, in front of the Capitol. What is the general's last name?

_____

.............................10 points ☐

2 Find Freedom, a woman wearing draperies holding a sword and wreath. (hint: Look up to the highest point on the Capitol.)

..........................10 points ☐

3 Find a bronze statue of King Kamehameha, donated by the state of Hawaii for inclusion in the National Statuary Hall.

....10 points ☐

4 Find George Washington in the fresco painted on the interior of the Capitol's dome. What is the figure

▲ The U.S. Capitol sits atop Capitol Hill.

The Capitol is home to the U.S. Congress and its two legislative bodies, the U.S. Senate and the U.S. House of Representatives.

THE NATION'S CAPITAL

The U. S. capital was originally located in Philadelphia, Pennsylvania. In the late 1700s, it was decided that our country needed a new capital separate from the states. After much debate, the site along the Potomac River was chosen by President George Washington.

French city planner Pierre L'Enfant was chosen by President Washington to design the new city. L'Enfant decided on a grid system with intersecting streets centered around the Capitol Building, which would stand at the top of a hill. His design included a garden-lined "grand avenue" in the center and canals filled with water. Eventually L'Enfant lost his job after too many disagreements and his design was changed, but much of his original grid plan can be seen today, including the tree-lined "grand avenue" that is now the National Mall.

▲ L'Enfant's "grand avenue," the National Mall.

next to him blowing?

_____

....10 points ☐

5 Ride the United States Capitol subway system below Capitol Hill.

....10 points ☐

6 Meet a senator or representative.

....10 points ☐

UNITED STATES BOTANIC GARDEN

If you want to escape the hustle and bustle of the city, head to the United States Botanic Garden. The garden sits on the grounds of the United States Capitol. It is one of the oldest botanic gardens in North America. With over 4,000 specimens on display, the United States Botanic Garden is like a museum for plants!

7 Use your nose to sniff out a vanilla and a chocolate tree. Yum!

....10 points ☐

8 Find a "living fossil" - the 200-million-year-old plant species called the cycad.

....10 points ☐

9 List one animal found on the fountain in Bartholdi Park. The fountain was created by Frederic Auguste Bartholdi, sculptor of the Statue of Liberty.

_____

....10 points ☐

10 Have your picture taken in the First Ladies Water Garden which pays tribute to the First Ladies of the United States. Its patterns are inspired by the Colonial–era quilt pattern known as "Martha Washington."

....10 points ☐

LIBRARY OF CONGRESS

The Library of Congress is the largest library in the world. When British troops burned the original library in 1814, Thomas Jefferson sold his personal collection of books to Congress as a replacement. What began as several thousand books from Jefferson's library has grown to millions of books, recordings, photographs, maps, and manuscripts. Although you can't check out a book to take home, everyone is welcome to browse and do research.

11 Find four turtles and a sea serpent having a water fight in the Court of Neptune Fountain. Neptune, the Roman god of the sea, watches from a bank of rocks.

....10 points ⬜

12 Visit the Great Hall in the Library of Congress. Find a large brass inlay in the center of the marble floor.

What is the shape of the inlay?

_____

....10 points ⬜

13 Visit the Main Reading Room. Look up and enjoy the view of the domed ceiling, stretching 160 feet above the reading room floor.

....10 points ⬜

14 Find a book from the 15th-century that was the first book printed using movable metal type. What is the name of this book?

_____

....10 points ⬜

SUPREME COURT BUILDING

Here comes the judge! The Supreme Court Building is the seat of the Supreme Court of the United States, the third branch of the U.S. government. All court sessions are open to the public, but you'll have to get in line early. Seating is on a first-come, first-served basis. When court is not in session, you can walk the Great Hall and visit the exhibit hall to learn about the Supreme Court and the justices that served on it. You can also watch a short movie about the judicial process in the theater.

15 Find the 4-word motto of the Supreme Court over the main entrance door. Write the motto here.

▲ Authority of Law statue outside the U.S. Supreme Court Building.

_____

_____

_____

_____

....10 points ☐

16 Find the two sculptures at the main entrance, the female figure *Contemplation of Justice* and the male figure *Authority of Law.*

....10 points ☐

The U.S. Supreme Court met in the United States Capitol until 1935, when it moved across the street into its own building.

17 How many marble columns stand at the entrance of the Supreme Court Building?

_____

....10 points ⬭

18 Find the bust of Chief Justice Rehnquist in the Great Hall.

....10 points ⬭

▲ Inside the main hall in Union Station.

Union Station opened on October 27, 1908, with the arrival of a B&O passenger train from Pittsburgh.

UNION STATION

When it was completed in 1908, Union Station was the largest train station in the world. The beautiful, ornate structure was modeled after buildings in ancient Rome, with marble corridors, columns, gold leaf, and sculptures. Each day hundreds of trains still pass through Union Station, but today you can also find shops, restaurants, and a movie theater within its walls. Union Station is one of the most-visited and best-known places in Washington, DC.

19 Find a memorial to an Italian

explorer who sailed across the Atlantic Ocean to the Americas in 1492. The three flags flying behind the memorial symbolize the three ships his crew sailed to the new world. Who was this explorer?

_____

....10 points ☐

20 In the early 1900's, the President and his family traveled across the United States by train. They would board the train in Union Station's Presidential Suite. Find the restaurant that now occupies the former Presidential Suite and write its name below.

_____

....10 points ☐

21 Count the row of Roman legionnaire (soldier) statues

overlooking the main hall of Union Station. How many statues are there?

_____

....10 points ☐

TOTAL POINTS FOR THIS SECTION

How did you do? Add up all your points from this section and write the number on the line below!

_____ **points**

NOTES

4 EXPLORING THE NATIONAL MALL

Many people begin their sightseeing in Washington, DC on the National Mall. This open, tree-lined area is one of the country's oldest national parks, originally part of Pierre L'Enfant's 1791 plan for the city. The Mall is home to many significant and historic buildings, most of which are free to visit. On the eastern end, the shimmering dome of the U.S. Capitol rises above Capitol Hill. To the west stands the stark white obelisk of the Washington Monument. Surrounding the park are world-class Smithsonian museums. The Mall is also a great place to just relax. It's a favorite hangout for picnickers, dog walkers, Frisbee players, joggers, and skaters. The National Mall is a fun place to visit inside or out!

SMITHSONIAN INFORMATION CENTER

The Smithsonian Information Center is also known as "The Castle" because it resembles a fairy tale castle. Head inside to learn all about the Institution's museums and National Zoo. Watch the short video, then check out the scale model of the city.

❶ Find a statue of the first Secretary of the Smithsonian. Write his name below.

_____

...................................10 points ☐

❷ Visit the Crypt Room and find the tomb of James Smithson, the man

▲ **Ride on an old-fashioned carousel.**

The Smithsonian Institute Building is constructed of red Seneca sandstone. It is nicknamed "The Castle."

who left his fortune to the United States to establish the Smithsonian Institution.

...................................10 points ☐

❸ Take a spin on the 1947 Smithsonian Carousel, located on the National Mall outside of the Smithsonian Castle.

...................................10 points ☐

NATIONAL AIR AND SPACE MUSEUM

If you like airplanes, spacecraft, or anything to do with outer space and flight, you'll love the National Air and Space Museum! The museum traces the history of flight and includes hundreds of rockets, planes, and spacecraft including the first powered aircraft built by Orville and Wilbur Wright in 1903. The National Air and Space Museum is one of the largest and most visited museums in the world!

❹ Find a rock from outer space. Where did this rock come from?

_____

....................................10 points ▢

❺ Find the 1903 Wright Flyer, the first powered aircraft designed, built, and flown by the Wright brothers. Where did the first flight take place?

_____

....................................10 points ▢

▲ Charles Lindbergh's *Spirit of St. Louis.*

The Apollo 11 space flight landed the first humans on the Moon on July 20, 1969.

6 Take one small step and one giant leap in front of the Apollo 11 Command Module that carried Buzz Aldrin, Neil Armstrong, and Michael Collins to the moon in 1969.

............................10 points ☐

7 Amelia Earhart was the first woman to fly solo across the Atlantic Ocean. Find the Red Vega airplane she piloted on her historic flight. In what year did she accomplish this feat?

_____

............................10 points ☐

8 Go inside SkyLab and pretend you are a scientist conducting research experiments in the United States' first space station.

............................10 points ☐

9 Find the *Spirit of St. Louis*, the airplane Charles Lindbergh used to make the first transatlantic flight in 1927.

............................10 points ☐

NATIONAL MUSEUM OF THE AMERICAN INDIAN

The National Museum of the American Indian is one of the newest Smithsonian museums and the only national museum dedicated to the Native American people. Its curved, golden limestone exterior, designed to resemble the natural rock formations of the desert Southwest, makes it easy to spot on the National Mall. Take time to stroll through the surrounding landscape - croplands, hardwood forests, and meadowland symbolizing the Native Americans' connection to the land.

10 Sit around the campfire in the Lelawi Theater and watch the multimedia presentation on American Indian life. What does "Lelawi" mean?

_____

.............................10 points ▢

11 Watch an ancient tribal music and dance performance.

.............................10 points ▢

12 Find a Hawaiian outrigger canoe. What type of wood is the canoe made from?

_____

Want to get up close and personal with some of the world's greatest art? Try a free audio tour designed just for kids available in the museum.

▲ Giant spider in the Sculpture Garden.

.............................10 points ▢

NATIONAL GALLERY OF ART

Contained within two buildings spanning four city blocks, the National Art Gallery is one big art museum! Many famous paintings and other works of art that you may have seen in books or on TV can be found in this museum.

13 Find the only painting by Leonardo da Vinci in the Western Hemisphere.

....10 points ☐

14 Look up to find a giant mobile by Alexander Calder. What is the name of Calder's sculpture?

_____

....10 points ☐

15 Find a work of art that makes you feel happy. Tell your parents why it makes you feel happy.

....10 points ☐

16 Take a ride in one of the museum's huge elevators. Find out why the elevators are so big. (hint: Ask a museum worker!)

_____

....10 points ☐

17 Photograph members of your family posing as outdoor sculpture in the Sculpture Garden across the street from the West Building. The Sculpture Garden is transformed into an ice rink in the winter!

....10 points ☐

NATIONAL MUSEUM OF NATURAL HISTORY

Where can you find an African Bush elephant, a North Atlantic right whale, and a prehistoric Triceratops? At the National Museum of Natural History! From animals, plants, and insects to fossils, rocks, and minerals, there are over 500 million specimens in the museum to explore.

18 Find the largest deep blue diamond in the world, the Hope Diamond. Did you know the Hope Diamond is over one billion years old?

....10 points ☐

19 Find a nest of dinosaur eggs.

....10 points ☐

20 Find a giant insect that hisses! What kind of insect is it?

_____

...........................10 points ▢

21 Play the role of a scientist and conduct an experiment in the Discovery Room.

...........................10 points ▢

22 Find an animal that lived during the Ice Age.

...........................10 points ▢

The ruby slippers on display are the actual shoes worn by Dorothy (played by Judy Garland) in the 1939 movie *The Wizard of Oz.*

▲ Lincoln wore this hat on the night he went to Ford's Theatre.

NATIONAL MUSEUM OF AMERICAN HISTORY

Where do you keep notes and papers that you want to keep handy? President Lincoln tucked important papers inside his top hat! You can see Lincoln's hat, and other American historic treasures, in the National Museum of American History.

23 Find Dorothy's ruby slippers from the movie *The Wizard of Oz*.

....10 points ☐

24 Find the original Star-Spangled Banner, the flag that flew over Fort McHenry during the War of 1812. Seeing the flag during the battle inspired Francis Scott Key to write the words to what famous anthem?

_____

....10 points ☐

25 Find part of a Disney ride inspired by a little cartoon elephant that could fly.

....10 points ☐

26 Find President Abraham Lincoln's black Stovepipe top hat.

....10 points ☐

27 Have your picture taken by a steam locomotive.

....10 points ☐

28 Find *Sesame Street* star Kermit the Frog.

....10 points ☐

29 Find the "Brown Box," a prototype for the first multiplayer video game system invented in 1969. Who is known as the "Father of the Video Game?"

_____

....10 points ☐

TOTAL POINTS FOR THIS SECTION

How did you do? Add up all your points from this section and write the number on the line below!

_____ **points**

NOTES

5 | A MONUMENTAL CHALLENGE

*T*he areas of West Potomac Park, which lies between the Washington Monument and the Lincoln Memorial, and the Tidal Basin region are home to the national monuments and memorials. Stand near the Reflecting Pool and you are standing in the middle of history. All around you stand monuments and memorials to some of America's greatest people and events. Historic rallies, such as the civil rights March on Washington for Jobs and Freedom (at which Martin Luther King, Jr. gave his famous "I Have a Dream" speech) occurred on this site. There is a lot to see, but even more to reflect upon.

VIETNAM VETERANS MEMORIAL

Completed in 1982, the Vietnam Veterans Memorial honors members of the U.S. armed forces who fought in the Vietnam War. Look for your reflection in the shiny black granite as you walk along the 250-foot long Memorial Wall. The wall is etched with the names of servicemen killed or missing in action during the Vietnam War. The memorial's designer chose the reflective black granite to help visitors connect the past (the etched names of Vietnam veterans) with the present (you).

❶ One end of the Memorial Wall points toward the Washington Monument. What does the other end point toward? (hint: It's another well-known monument.)

_____

............................10 points ☐

❷ Find the name of a serviceman

Your reflection over the engraved names on the wall symbolically brings the past and present together.

on the wall that has the same first name as a member of your family. Write the name of the serviceman below.

_____

....10 points ☐

❸ Find a bronze statue of three soldiers that appear to be looking at

▲ **Take time to reflect at the Vietnam Veterans Memorial Wall.**

the names of their comrades on the wall. This statue, named *The Three Soldiers*, was placed in 1984 to complement the Memorial Wall.

....10 points ⃝

❹ Find the Vietnam Women's Memorial, located a short distance south of the wall. The statue, which honors women who served in the war, depicts nurses tending to a wounded soldier.

▲ Lincoln Memorial illuminated at night.

....10 points ⃝

LINCOLN MEMORIAL

The Lincoln Memorial was dedicated in 1922 to honor the 16th President of the United States, Abraham Lincoln. Inside is a large marble statue of Lincoln sitting in a chair. The statue stands 19 feet high and is 19 feet wide! Text from two of Lincoln's well-known speeches, the Gettysburg Address and Lincoln's second inaugural address, are inscribed on the walls inside the memorial. The Lincoln Memorial has been the site

A popular legend claims Lincoln is using sign language to form his initials - an "A" with his left hand and an "L" with his right hand.

of many famous events, including Martin Luther King, Jr.'s "I Have a Dream" speech during the March on Washington in 1963.

5 Find the spot on the front steps of the Lincoln Memorial where Martin Luther King, Jr. delivered his "I Have a Dream" speech. Gaze out over the Reflecting Pool and imagine Dr. King speaking to over 200,000 civil rights supporters at this very spot.

....10 points ◯

6 44-foot tall Greek Doric columns surround the Lincoln Memorial. How many columns are there?

_____

....10 points ◯

7 Find a U.S. coin and a U.S. paper bill that feature the Lincoln Memorial on the reverse side.

_____

_____

....10 points ◯

NATIONAL WORLD WAR II MEMORIAL

The National World War II Memorial is dedicated to servicemen and civilians who served during World War II. It is located at the eastern end of the Reflecting Pool, between the Lincoln Memorial and the Washington Monument. Dedicated in 2004, it is one of the newest monuments on the National Mall.

8 The National World War II Memorial consists of 56 granite pillars arranged in a semicircle around a plaza, each engraved with the name of one of the 48 U.S. states and other U.S. territories of 1945. Find the pillars for the two U.S.

territories that later became our 49th and 50th states. Write their names below.

_____

_____

..............................10 points ☐

❾ "Kilroy was here" was a popular expression during World War II. U. S. servicemen often wrote the saying on walls where they were

▲ **Rainbow Pool fountain at the National World War II Memorial.**

The National World War II Memorial was dedicated by President George W. Bush on May 29, 2004, two days before Memorial Day.

stationed along with a picture of a bald-headed man with a large nose peeking over a wall. Find the engraving of Kilroy on the World War II Memorial.

..............................10 points ☐

❿ Find the Freedom Wall with over 4,000 gold stars, each representing 100 Americans who died in the war. About how many Americans died? (hint: You need to multiply. Ask your parents if you need help!)

_____

..............................10 points ⬭

KOREAN WAR VETERANS MEMORIAL

The Korean War Veterans Memorial honors those who served in the Korean War. The memorial is in the form of a triangle intersecting a circle. Can you find the shapes? Within the triangle are 19 stainless steel statues of a squad on patrol in Korea. If you look closely at the long, black granite wall, you can see images of soldiers, equipment, and people involved in the war.

11 Find the statues of a squad of servicemen. How many servicemen are on patrol?

_____

..............................10 points ⬭

12 Find the United Nations Wall. This low wall lists the 22 members of the United Nations that contributed troops or medical support during the Korean war.

..............................10 points ⬭

13 Find the Pool of Remembrance which lists the numbers killed, wounded, missing in action, and held as prisoners of war. How many Americans died in the Korean War?

_____

..............................10 points ⬭

FRANKLIN DELANO ROOSEVELT MEMORIAL

President Franklin D. Roosevelt led the United States through some of its hardest times, including the Great Depression and World War I. The Franklin Delano Roosevelt Memorial, located along the Cherry Tree Walk on the edge of the Tidal Basin, celebrates President Roosevelt's life and accomplishments. As you walk through the memorial you will revisit twelve years of American history through four outdoor rooms depicting scenes from President Roosevelt's terms in office. Look for the waterfalls in each room. Like the problems that President Roosevelt faced in his years in office, the waterfalls get larger and more complex as you move through each room in the memorial.

14 Find the statue of President Roosevelt's dog, Fala.

..............................10 points ☐

15 Find a sculpture of men waiting in a bread line during the Great Depression. How many men are waiting in line?

_____

..............................10 points ☐

16 Find a statue of First Lady Eleanor Roosevelt standing before the United Nations emblem. This statue honors Eleanor Roosevelt's dedication to the UN and is the only presidential memorial to depict a First Lady.

..............................10 points ☐

17 Find a wall engraved with the "Four Freedoms" - four fundamental freedoms that President Roosevelt believed people throughout the world should enjoy. Complete the freedoms below.

Freedom of _____

Freedom of _____

Freedom from _____

Freedom from _____

..............................10 points ☐

JEFFERSON MEMORIAL

The Jefferson Memorial is dedicated to the

3rd President of the United States, Thomas Jefferson. Jefferson was also one of the founding fathers of America. The memorial sits on the shore of the Potomac River Tidal Basin. Under the memorial's white dome stands a 19-foot high statue of Jefferson. Because bronze was in high demand during World War II when the memorial was completed, the original statue was created in plaster. It was later replaced with the bronze one that now stands at the center.

18 Find the excerpt from the Declaration of Independence, written by Jefferson in 1776, on the inside wall of the memorial. Complete the sentence below:

"We hold these truths to be self-evident, that all men _____

_____ "

....10 points ⬜

▲ **Jefferson Memorial on the shore of the Tidal Basin.**

President Franklin Roosevelt, an admirer of Jefferson, requested the erection of the memorial in 1934.

19 Thomas Jefferson believed that all men are born with certain rights that no one can take away. Complete this phrase from the Declaration of Independence:

"they are endowed by their Creator with certain unalienable Rights, that among these are _____, _____, and _____ "

..............................10 points ☐

20 Find one of the many Japanese cherry trees outside the Jefferson

▲ **U.S. flags surround the Washington Monument.**

Memorial. These trees were a gift from the people of Japan in 1912.

..............................10 points ☐

The Washington Monument was the world's tallest structure until 1889, when the Eiffel Tower was completed in Paris, France.

UNITED STATES HOLOCAUST MEMORIAL MUSEUM

The United States Holocaust Memorial Museum is a living memorial honoring the

victims and survivors of the Holocaust. The museum was created to share knowledge about this tragedy and the lessons learned as well as to preserve the memory of those who suffered. On the first floor, you can visit "Remember the Children: Daniel's Story," an exhibition presenting the history of the Holocaust for elementary and middle school children.

21 Compare Daniel's room to your own room at home. List one thing that is similar.

_____

....10 points ☐

22 Find Daniel's January 20, 1933 diary entry. Why won't some of Daniel's friends play with him?

_____

_____

....10 points ☐

23 Find the ghetto where Daniel was sent along with thousands of Jews. What three words would you use to describe the ghetto?

_____

_____

_____

....10 points ☐

WASHINGTON MONUMENT

It's hard to miss the Washington Monument. It's the tallest stone structure in the world and the tallest building in Washington, DC standing over 550 feet! The monument is made of marble, granite, and sandstone. It was built in honor of the first U.S. President, General George Washington. When it first opened in 1885, visitors had to climb the 897-step stairway to the top. Whew! Today you can ride the elevator for a 360 degree view of the city!

24 Count the circle of American flags around the base of the monument. How many are there?

_____

....10 points ☐

25 Find a bronze statue of General Washington inside the monument.

....10 points ☐

26 The monument's white marble exterior has two different shades

▲ **Watch money being printed at the Bureau of Engraving and Printing.**

Don't look for coins at the Bureau of Engraving and Printing. Coins are produced at the U.S. Mint.

because it took about 50 years to finish. Construction of the monument started in 1848. In 1854, the project was halted due to lack of funding and the Civil War. Over 20 years later, construction resumed using marble from different quarries. Find the change of color about one-third of the way up the monument.

....10 points ☐

BUREAU OF ENGRAVING AND PRINTING

Amid all the monuments in the National Mall stands the Bureau of Engraving and Printing. It is where United States paper currency is made. The bureau prints billions of dollars each year! You can take a free tour and watch real money being printed. Follow along as large, blank sheets of paper are transformed into U.S. bills.

27 Find a printing press used to print money.

..............................10 points ☐

28 Find a large, uncut sheet of U.S. bills.

..............................10 points ☐

29 Find a machine that uses cameras to examine sheets of bills for defects.

..............................10 points ☐

30 Find a $100,000 bill.

..............................10 points ☐

31 List two things other than money that are printed at the Bureau of Engraving and Printing.

_____

_____

..............................10 points ☐

TOTAL POINTS FOR THIS SECTION

How did you do? Add up all your points from this section and write the number on the line below!

_____ **points**

NOTES

6

THE WHITE HOUSE & FOGGY BOTTOM

Who's the most famous person in Washington, DC? The President, of course! Get a glimpse at what it's like to be the commander-in-chief by visiting the White House, the official residence and primary workplace of the President of the United States. When he's not working, you may find the President attending a performance at the nearby Kennedy Center for the Performing Arts. You and your family can also enjoy a performance at the Kennedy Center, or stroll its vast interior, decorated with sculptures, carvings, tapestries, and other gifts from countries around the world.

WHITE HOUSE VISITOR CENTER

The White House Visitor Center not only serves as the starting point for tours, but it's also a great place to learn more about the White House. You can see a 30-minute video and explore exhibits featuring many aspects of the White House, including its architecture, furnishings, first families, and a behind-the-scenes look at the chefs, gardeners, servants, Secret Service people, and others who work there.

1 Find out who conducted an aviation demonstration at the White House in 1911.

_____

....10 points ☐

2 Find a photo of the Oval Office, the official office of the President of the United States located in the West Wing of the White House.

The White House was originally a natural gray color. It took 570 gallons of white paint to cover its outside surface.

▲ **The White House viewed from atop the Washington Monument.**

....10 points ☐

3 Read about the various jobs of people who work at the White House. If you worked at the White House, which job would you do?

_____

....10 points ☐

THE WHITE HOUSE

In the late 1790s, while the city of Washington, DC was being developed, a house for the President was also being planned. President George Washington chose the location, although he never lived there. The house wasn't completed until John Adams was president in 1800.

▲ **The White House in 1846.**

When Adams moved in, only six rooms had been finished. Today there are 132 rooms and 35 bathrooms on 6 levels. There are also 28 fireplaces, 8 staircases, and 3 elevators! Over the years, presidents have added a variety of recreational facilities, including a bowling alley, a movie theater, a swimming pool, and a putting green.

Originally known as the "President's House," President Theodore Roosevelt officially renamed it the White House in 1901.

THE WHITE HOUSE

The White House is the official residence of the President of the United States. George Washington chose the location for the house in 1790. It has been the home of every U.S. President since John Adams. Did you know it was not always called the White House? It was originally referred to as the "President's House" or "President's Palace."

4 Find the south fountain, located on the south lawn of the White House. The White House uses the south lawn to host the annual Easter egg roll and other outdoor activities.

....10 points ☐

5 Find a portrait of a president in the White House. Who did you find?

_____

....10 points ☐

6 Find a room that's used for large parties and receptions. What is the name of this room?

_____

....10 points ☐

7 Find the White House State Dining Room, which is used during formal dinners for visiting heads of state. How many guests can be seated in this room?

_____

....10 points ☐

8 Find the National Christmas Tree in the Ellipse, a circular park just south of the White House. This tree is lit each year by the President at the start of the holiday season.

....10 points ☐

NATIONAL AQUARIUM

The National Aquarium is the oldest aquarium in the nation. It has been located in the lower level of the Department of Commerce Building since 1931. The aquarium is home to more than 200 species including alligators, piranhas, and sharks.

9 Look closely to find an eight-armed Giant Pacific Octopus - a highly intelligent animal and a master of camouflage!

..............................10 points ☐

10 Find the Florida Everglades National Marine Sanctuary exhibit. List one thing that threatens the Florida Everglades' survival.

_____

..............................10 points ☐

11 Find two animals that live in a bog

environment.

_____

_____

..............................10 points ☐

LAFAYETTE SQUARE

Lafayette Square is a public park located just north of the White House. It was originally part of the White House grounds until President Jefferson had Pennsylvania Avenue cut through the south lawn in 1804. The park has been used for many things, including a slave market, a zoo, and a race track. During the War of 1812, it was used as an encampment for soldiers. Today it is designated a National Historic Landmark.

12 Find St. John's Episcopal Church, also known as "The Church of the Presidents" because every president since James Madison has attended service there.

..............................10 points ☐

13 Find the President's Pew in St. John's Episcopal Church, reserved for the chief executive's use when in attendance. What number is the President's Pew?

..............................10 points ☐

14 Whose statue stands at the center of Lafayette Square? (hint: He was the 7th President of the United States.)

The bell in St. John's steeple was cast by Paul Revere's son, Joseph, at his Boston foundry in 1822. It weighs nearly 1,000 pounds.

..............................10 points ☐

KENNEDY CENTER FOR THE PERFORMING ARTS

The Kennedy Center is America's living memorial to President John F. Kennedy and the nation's busiest arts facility. President Kennedy was a great supporter of the arts. Each year the Kennedy Center presents

▲ "The Church of the Presidents" - St. John's Episcopal Church in Lafayette Square.

thousands of theater, dance, music, and multi-media performances for all ages.

⑮ Many gifts have been given to the Kennedy Center by other countries over the years. Find

...a 50-foot diameter chandelier in the Opera House (a gift from Austria).

..............................10 points ☐

▲ Bronze bust of John F. Kennedy.

...a sculpture of Don Quixote dressed in a suit of armor astride his horse on the east lawn (a gift from Spain).

..............................10 points ☐

...a room with jagged ceilings and slanted walls made to represent an African village (a gift from the nations of Africa). What is the name of this room?

_____

..............................10 points ☐

In 1960, John F. Kennedy became the youngest person elected President of the United States. He was forty-three years old.

16 Find an eight foot bronze bust of John F. Kennedy in the Grand Foyer.

....10 points ⬭

17 Find the Family Theater and watch a performance. What show did you see?

_____

....10 points ⬭

18 Complete the quote below by President Kennedy found on the wall of the River Terrace.

"I look forward to an America which will not be afraid of

_____

and _____ "

....10 points ⬭

TOTAL POINTS FOR THIS SECTION

How did you do? Add up all your points from this section and write the number on the line below!

_____ **points**

NOTES

7 | PENN QUARTER PUZZLER

One hundred years ago, Penn Quarter was the heart of the city. Today, the hustle and bustle of horse and carriages is gone, but there is still plenty to see and do in the area. The National Archives is a must-do stop on a visit to Washington, DC. Inside you can see historic documents like the Declaration of Independence. Ford's Theatre was a busy performing arts center in the 1800s, but today it's better known as the place where Abraham Lincoln was assassinated in 1865. You can visit the theatre and view the Presidential Box where Lincoln was shot. And if you've ever had the urge to become a secret agent, you can attend the School for Spies at the International Spy Museum. Are you ready for your top-secret mission?

NATIONAL ARCHIVES

The National Archives was created to preserve the nation's most important paper documents. Among the historic artifacts you can see are the three major documents on which the United States government was founded - the Constitution, the Declaration of Independence, and the Bill of Rights. Also on display is one of only four remaining copies of the Magna Carta of 1297. In addition, the Public Vault contains many more historical documents and photos.

The National Archives is an important research center for those tracing their family roots.

1 Find

...the Declaration of Independence.

...........................10 points ☐

...the Constitution.

...........................10 points ☐

...the Bill of Rights.

...........................10 points ☐

2 Find Thomas Jefferson in a mural in the Rotunda. What is he handing to John Hancock?

_____

...........................10 points ☐

▲ **Declaration of Independence on display in the National Archives.**

3 Find out what happens to these

important documents at night when the National Archives closes.

_____

_____

_____

....10 points ▢

FORD'S THEATRE

Ford's Theatre is an historic theatre from the 1800s. It is also the site of one of the country's most tragic events. On April 14, 1865, while watching a performance, President Abraham

You can still enjoy a show at Ford's Theatre today. The theatre is both a national historic site and a performing arts center.

Lincoln was assassinated in Ford's Theatre by actor John Wilkes Booth. Today, you can tour Ford's Theatre, as well as the Petersen House across the street where Lincoln was carried and later died the next morning.

❹ Find the Presidential Box where President Lincoln was shot.

....10 points ▢

▲ Lincoln's Presidential Box in Ford's Theatre.

5 Find the alley where John Wilkes Booth escaped. What was he riding when he made his escape?

_____

....10 points ☐

6 Find a plaque on the wall of the Petersen House commemorating the site of Lincoln's death on April 15, 1865. What time did Abraham Lincoln die?

_____

....10 points ☐

FREEDOM PLAZA

Freedom Plaza is an open public space located at the corner of 14th Street and Pennsylvania Avenue. It is a popular place for political protests and other public events. Look for parts of Pierre L'Enfant's original plan for the City of Washington inlaid in stone on the plaza.

7 Find the Freedom Plaza Marker. Who is Freedom Plaza named in honor of?

_____

....10 points ☐

8 Find out what was buried at the site in January 1988.

_____

....10 points ☐

9 Visit the lobby of the Willard Hotel, located at the end of the plaza, where Martin Luther King, Jr. wrote his historic "I Have a Dream" speech.

....10 points ☐

U.S. NAVY MEMORIAL

This single bronze statue of a sailor is a

memorial to the men and women who have served in the U.S. Navy. The statue stands on a map of the world surrounded by naval flags with waterfalls and fountains containing water from the seven seas.

❿ Find *The Lone Sailor* statue. Follow his gaze. What do you believe he is thinking about?

▲ *The Lone Sailor* at the U.S. Navy Memorial.

_____

_____

....10 points ☐

⓫ Find a bronze panel honoring the United States Coast Guard.

....10 points ☐

The bronze for The Lone Sailor was mixed with artifacts from eight U. S. Navy ships.

NATIONAL PORTRAIT GALLERY

Visit the National Portrait Gallery to view paintings of famous Americans. Collections are diverse - from American presidents to historic figures such as Charles Lindbergh *and Henry Ford. You'll even find images of sports stars like Shaquille O'Neal and Vince Lombardi. Don't miss the Hall of Presidents, the nation's collection of the official portraits of the presidents.*

12 Find a rainbow in the famous Lansdowne portrait of George Washington. The rainbow symbolizes the end of the stormy days of the American Revolution.

....10 points ☐

13 Find a famous photograph of Abraham Lincoln taken just two months before his assassination in 1865. Where is President Lincoln in the photo?

_____

_____

....10 points ☐

14 Find two of the tiniest portraits at the National Portrait Gallery - engravings of George Washington from 1798 that are about the size of a fingernail!

....10 points ☐

INTERNATIONAL SPY MUSEUM

Become a secret agent and sneak around the International Spy Museum to see the most extensive collection of spy gear in the world. Watch what you say - hidden microphones pick up your every word! Visit the "Tricks of the Trade" exhibit to view actual devices used by spies to disguise and protect them in their missions. Watch out for museum guides acting as police - you may be questioned about your assumed identity.

15 Find a buttonhole camera in the "School for Spies."

....10 points ☐

16 Find the "Secret History of History" exhibit. Who was known as the "Father of the KGB?"

_____

....10 points ☐

17 Decode a secret message using the WWII German enigma machine. Write the message below.

_____

_____

_____

_____

_____

_____

_____

....10 points ☐

▲ Inside the National Portrait Gallery.

The building that houses the National Portrait Gallery served as a makeshift hospital during the Civil War.

TOTAL POINTS FOR THIS SECTION

*How did you do? Add up all your points
from this section and write the number on
the line below!*

_____ **points**

NOTES

8

OUT & ABOUT

*A*lthough the majority of sites in Washington, DC are located in the center of town near the National Mall, there are plenty of things you don't want to miss outside the city center. The National Zoo in Rock Creek Park is a kid-favorite. Who doesn't love giant pandas? Washington National Cathedral is one of the largest church buildings in the world. It's so large, you could fit a football field inside! And if you love the outdoors, you have to visit the nation's garden, the U.S. National Arboretum. It's a great place to take a hike, bicycle its winding roads, or just hang out and enjoy nature.

NATIONAL ZOO

The National Zoo is one of the oldest zoos in the United States. Founded in 1889, the zoo is home to over 2000 animals, including the popular giant pandas on loan from the China Wildlife Conservation Association. Officially titled the Smithsonian National Zoological Park, the zoo is part of the Smithsonian Institution.

1 Find the giant pandas. List one reason why the giant pandas are endangered.

_____

_____

_____

..........................10 points ☐

2 Find the Asia Trail. List five of the animal species on exhibit.

_____

> **About one-fifth of the animals at the Smithsonian National Zoological Park are endangered or threatened.**

▲ **Visit the pandas at the National Zoo.**

_____

_____

_____

_____

..........................10 points ☐

3 Look up and find an orangutan traveling on the O Line between the Great Ape House and Think Tank.

..........................10 points ☐

❹ Find out how pizza ingredients are grown in the Pizza Garden. Then list your favorite topping found in the garden.

_____

....10 points ⬭

❺ Have your picture taken in front of your favorite animal at the zoo.

....10 points ⬭

WASHINGTON NATIONAL CATHEDRAL

Washington National Cathedral is the sixth

▲ **Looking up at Washington National Cathedral.**

largest cathedral in the world. Its central nave is longer than a football field! Due to its role over the years in uniting Americans through religious and other services, Congress has designated the Washington National Cathedral as the "National House of Prayer."

Climb the cathedral's central tower to the observation deck for sweeping views of the surrounding city.

6 Find the Space Window, honoring man's landing on the Moon. What is embedded in the center of the window?

....10 points ☐

7 Find the tomb of an American president. Who is buried there?

....10 points ☐

8 Find a character from *Star Wars* on the northwest tower of the Cathedral. Who did you find?

....10 points ☐

9 Find a stained glass window with the same name as a flower. What is the name of the window?

....10 points ☐

U.S. NATIONAL ARBORETUM

You can escape the hustle and bustle of Washington, DC in the U.S. National Arboretum, also known as the nation's garden. The Arboretum is a big place - about the size of 339 football fields - that showcases a collection of plants and trees that are special in some way.

10 Find a "sad" tree that is weeping and blue. What kind of tree is it?

....10 points ☐

11 Find the oldest tree at the Arboretum. (hint: It came from Japan and is almost 400 years old!)

....10 points ☐

⓬ Find a koi. (hint: It looks like a giant goldfish.)

.....................................10 points ☐

⓭ Find the biggest tree at the Arboretum that has been growing since the Civil War! What kind of tree is it?

_____

.....................................10 points ☐

ARLINGTON NATIONAL CEMETERY

Arlington National Cemetery is the final resting spot for many men and women who served in the United States military. The cemetery is a place to honor and remember the nation's veterans.

⓮ Find the Tomb of the Unknowns, also known as the "Tomb of the Unknown Soldier," and complete the inscription:

"Here rests in honored glory an

_____

_____

_____"

.....................................10 points ☐

⓯ Read the poem on the memorial honoring the crew of the Space Shuttle Challenger. What is the name of the poem?

_____

.....................................10 points ☐

⓰ Find the John F. Kennedy Eternal Flame. How many days a year does the flame burn?

_____

.....................................10 points ☐

IWO JIMA MEMORIAL

Iwo Jima is a small island near Tokyo, Japan. It was the last territory that U.S. troops recaptured from the Japanese during World War II. The Iwo Jima Memorial was inspired by an actual photograph of the flag raising by a group of Marines and a Navy hospital corpsman that signaled the successful capture of the island.

17 Read the engraved words on the memorial. The Iwo Jima Memorial honors the members of which branch of the armed forces?

_____

..............................10 points ⬭

18 How many soldiers are raising the flag?

_____

..............................10 points ⬭

19 Find an inscription in a wreath and

▲ Tomb of the Unknowns at Arlington National Cemetery.

The Tomb of the Unknowns is one of the most visited sites at Arlington National Cemetery. Three unknown servicemen are buried there.

complete the line:

"Uncommon valor was a

_____

_____"

..............................10 points ☐

THEODORE ROOSEVELT ISLAND

Theodore Roosevelt loved the outdoors. As president, he worked to preserve and protect public lands for forests, national parks, and wildlife sanctuaries. Theodore Roosevelt Island, with its miles of nature trails and boardwalk through forest and swamp, is a fitting memorial to the 26th U.S. President.

20 Find a 17-foot bronze statue of President Roosevelt in the center of the island.

..............................10 points ☐

21 Find a quote from President Roosevelt about nature.

..............................10 points ☐

▲ Nature abounds on Theodore Roosevelt Island.

No cars or bicycles are permitted on Theodore Roosevelt Island.

㉒ Take a hike on a nature trail.

...............................10 points ☐

㉓ List one way you can help preserve the environment.

_____

_____

...............................10 points ☐

THE PENTAGON AND PENTAGON MEMORIAL

The Pentagon is the headquarters of the U.S. Department of Defense. The building got its name from its unique five-sided design. It is the world's largest office building with over 17 miles of corridors! Just southwest of the Pentagon, a two-acre memorial park honors those lives lost on September 11, 2001, when American Airlines Flight 77 crashed into the western side of the Pentagon.

㉔ Find the Pentagon Memorial dedication tablet. Who does the memorial pay tribute to?

_____

...............................10 points ☐

㉕ Find the fire-scorched memorial entry threshold, made from the original walls of the Pentagon. What is engraved on the stone?

_____

...............................10 points ☐

㉖ Find a bench honoring the youngest victim of the attack.

...............................10 points ☐

TOTAL POINTS FOR THIS SECTION

How did you do? Add up all your points from this section and write the number on the line below!

_____ **points**

NOTES

PARENT CLUES

Parents, here is your chance to contribute to the hunt! Use the spaces below to add additional clues for your child to solve in and around Washington, DC. Try including places to find, foods to try, or experiences to enjoy. Have fun!

10 points ☐

10 points ☐

10 points ☐

10 points ☐

10 points ☐

10 points ☐

10 points ☐

10 points ☐

10 points ☐

10 points ☐

10 points ☐

10 points ☐

10 points ☐

10 points ☐

10 points ☐

10 points ☐

10 points ☐

10 points ☐

10 points ☐

NOTES

HOW DID YOU DO?

It's time to be rewarded for all your hard work! Use the area below to add up your total points from each section. Then add up your grand total and claim your award! Fill out your name and today's date on the award certificate. Then have your mom or dad sign it. Great job!!

CAPITOL HILL HUNT _____ POINTS

EXPLORING THE NATIONAL MALL _____ POINTS

A MONUMENTAL CHALLENGE _____ POINTS

THE WHITE HOUSE & FOGGY BOTTOM _____ POINTS

PENN QUARTER PUZZLER _____ POINTS

OUT & ABOUT _____ POINTS

_____ **TOTAL POINTS**

550-849 POINTS .... TRAVEL GUIDE
850-1099 POINTS .... TRAVEL ADVENTURER
1100+ POINTS .... WORLD EXPLORER

CERTIFICATE OF TRAVEL EXCELLENCE

This award certifies that

_____

has successfully achieved the level of

TRAVEL GUIDE

in Scavenger Guides Washington, DC Scavenger Adventure

_____   _____
DATE   PARENT

TRAVEL GUIDE
550-849 POINTS

CERTIFICATE OF TRAVEL EXCELLENCE

This award certifies that

_____

has successfully achieved the level of

TRAVEL ADVENTURER

in Scavenger Guides Washington, DC Scavenger Adventure

_____   _____
DATE   PARENT

TRAVEL ADVENTURER
850-1099 POINTS

CERTIFICATE OF TRAVEL EXCELLENCE

This award certifies that

_____

has successfully achieved the level of

WORLD EXPLORER

in Scavenger Guides Washington, DC Scavenger Adventure

_____   _____

DATE   PARENT

WORLD EXPLORER
1100+ POINTS

KEEPING A TRAVEL JOURNAL

Keeping a journal of your travel adventures is a wonderful way to preserve memories. It makes a great souvenir of your trip to Washington, DC! The following section of this guide provides you with space to record your daily writings.

Make a habit to write in your travel journal each night before bed. As you record your thoughts, reflect back on your day. Use your five senses to describe your adventures! What did you see? What smells filled your nose? Are there sounds that caught your attention? What tastes did you experience? What touches and textures do you remember?

If possible, take pictures each day during your travels. Photographs from your trip will complement your journal. If you do not have a camera of your own, ask your parents if you can be involved taking pictures with them.

When you return home, be sure to check out the free digital story tutorials on the Scavenger Guides website. You will learn how to combine recordings of your daily journal writings with digital pictures from your trip to create a multimedia travel video starring you! Visit http://www.scavengerguides.com to learn how!

The following page shows a sample journal entry. This is only an example. Feel free to record anything you wish from your travel experiences. Have fun with your journal!

MY TRAVEL JOURNAL   DAY 1

DATE _August 12_

SIGHTS _monuments, lots of people, Reflecting Pool_

SMELLS _flowers in the park, pizza!!_

SOUNDS _carousel music, cars honking, people talking_

TASTES _salty popcorn, sweet candy_

TOUCHES _cold water, soft grass_

DAILY LOG

Today we walked through the National Mall. We went up in the

Washington Monument and looked down on the White House and

Capitol Building. The view was awesome! Then we visited the Lincoln

Memorial. My dad took my picture on the spot where Martin Luther

King, Jr. gave his famous speech. My brother and I splashed each other

by the Reflecting Pool. We got really wet, but it was a lot of fun!

MY TRAVEL JOURNAL

DAY 1

DATE _____

SIGHTS_____

SMELLS_____

SOUNDS_____

TASTES_____

TOUCHES_____

DAILY LOG

_____

_____

_____

_____

_____

_____

MY TRAVEL JOURNAL   DAY 2

DATE _____

SIGHTS_____

SMELLS_____

SOUNDS_____

TASTES_____

TOUCHES_____

DAILY LOG

_____

_____

_____

_____

_____

_____

MY TRAVEL JOURNAL   DAY 3

DATE _____

SIGHTS_____

SMELLS_____

SOUNDS_____

TASTES_____

TOUCHES_____

DAILY LOG

_____

_____

_____

_____

_____

_____

My Travel Journal   Day 4

Date _____

Sights_____

Smells_____

Sounds_____

Tastes_____

Touches_____

Daily Log

_____

_____

_____

_____

_____

_____

MY TRAVEL JOURNAL

DAY 5

DATE _____

SIGHTS_____

SMELLS_____

SOUNDS_____

TASTES_____

TOUCHES_____

DAILY LOG

_____

_____

_____

_____

_____

_____

MY TRAVEL JOURNAL

DATE _____

SIGHTS _____

SMELLS _____

SOUNDS _____

TASTES _____

TOUCHES _____

DAILY LOG

_____

_____

_____

_____

_____

_____

MY TRAVEL JOURNAL   DAY 7

DATE _____

SIGHTS_____

SMELLS_____

SOUNDS_____

TASTES_____

TOUCHES_____

DAILY LOG

_____

_____

_____

_____

_____

_____

MY TRAVEL JOURNAL   **DAY 8**

DATE _____

SIGHTS_____

SMELLS_____

SOUNDS_____

TASTES_____

TOUCHES_____

DAILY LOG

_____

_____

_____

_____

_____

_____

My Travel Journal   Day 9

Date _____

Sights_____

Smells_____

Sounds_____

Tastes_____

Touches_____

Daily Log

_____

_____

_____

_____

_____

_____

MY TRAVEL JOURNAL   **DAY 10**

DATE _____

SIGHTS_____

SMELLS_____

SOUNDS_____

TASTES_____

TOUCHES_____

DAILY LOG

_____

_____

_____

_____

_____

_____

MY TRAVEL JOURNAL   DAY 11

DATE _____

SIGHTS_____

SMELLS_____

SOUNDS_____

TASTES_____

TOUCHES_____

DAILY LOG

_____

_____

_____

_____

_____

_____

MY TRAVEL JOURNAL   DAY 12

DATE _____

SIGHTS_____

SMELLS_____

SOUNDS_____

TASTES_____

TOUCHES_____

DAILY LOG

_____

_____

_____

_____

_____

_____

MY TRAVEL JOURNAL   **DAY 13**

DATE _____

SIGHTS_____

SMELLS_____

SOUNDS_____

TASTES_____

TOUCHES_____

DAILY LOG

_____

_____

_____

_____

_____

_____

MY TRAVEL JOURNAL   DAY 14

DATE _____

SIGHTS_____

SMELLS_____

SOUNDS_____

TASTES_____

TOUCHES_____

DAILY LOG

_____

_____

_____

_____

_____

_____

MY TOP 10

Earlier we gave you our picks for the Top 10 Things for Kids in Washington, DC. Now it's your turn! Think about all the things you did in Washington, DC. What were your favorites? Use the space below to record your picks for the best things to do in Washington, DC. Complete this page the last day of your visit. You can share this list with your friends when they plan their own Washington, DC adventure!

#10 _____

_____

#9 _____

_____

#8 _____

_____

#7 _____

_____

#6 _____

_____

#5 _____

_____

#4 _____

_____

#3 _____

_____

#2 _____

_____

#1 _____

_____

TIPS FOR TAKING GREAT VACATION PHOTOS

In addition to keeping a daily journal, you may also wish to take pictures during your travels. While your journal is a written record of your travel experiences, images are snapshots in time - visual memories to enjoy and share with others long after your vacation is over. Photographs from your trip will complement your journal and help you relive those great vacation memories!

This chapter will give you tips on how to take great vacation photos. Practice these techniques and soon you'll be taking shots like the pros. Above all, experiment and have fun with your photography!

FUN CREATIVE PROJECTS

After you return from your vacation you'll want to share your photos with family and friends. Pictures make wonderful souvenirs, and they are a great way to share your vacation experiences with others. There are also many things that you can do with your photos. Here are some fun activities you might consider.

✔ Create a framed collage of your favorite vacation photos to hang in your room.

✔ Design a vacation scrapbook.

✔ Create an online gallery to display your trip photos.

✔ Make your own vacation souvenir. Many online photo stores allow you to upload your digital pictures and place them on shirts, mugs, mouse pads, and other items.

✔ Combine your digital pictures and journal writings with motion effects and music to create a multimedia travel video to share with family and friends. Visit http://www. scavengerguides.com to learn how!

DON'T HAVE A CAMERA?

If you do not have a camera of your own, ask your parents if you can be involved taking pictures with them. Have your parents show you how to operate the camera. Ask if you can take some practice photos at home with their assistance. Another option is to use a disposable or single-use camera. These cameras come pre-loaded with a fixed number of photos (usually 24 or 36). When all of the pictures are taken, the entire camera is returned for processing. Single-use cameras are widely available for less than $10.

A MESSAGE FOR PARENTS

If possible, give your child their own camera to use. If that's not feasible, let them share the picture taking responsibilities with you. Spend some time before your trip showing them how to operate your camera correctly and responsibly. Have your child read the tips in this chapter, but don't over-supervise. Allow them the freedom to compose and take their own photos. You may be surprised at the pictures they take. Not only will you have a visual history of your trip from your child's perspective, but you may also find yourself in a few more vacation photos! While they certainly will enjoy the pictures you take, the experience and memories will mean more if they are fully involved in the process.

TIP #1: KNOW HOW TO USE YOUR CAMERA & SETTINGS

It's important that you know how to operate your camera before you go on your vacation. A lot of problems can be avoided if you know how your camera and all its settings work before you leave home. Here is a checklist of things to review.

▲ Take time before your trip to learn all the settings and features on your camera.

✔ Read the instructions that came with your camera, or ask your mom and dad to show you how their camera works. Know what settings to use for various shots.

✔ If your camera has a telephoto lens, find out how to zoom in and out.

✔ Learn how your flash works.

✔ Find out if there are any special features such as autofocus or red-eye reduction that can help you take better pictures.

✔ Practice using your camera by taking some pictures at home before your trip. This will help you get comfortable with your camera and learn what you can do with it.

✔ Practice keeping the camera still while taking pictures to prevent blurry photos. Breathe in while holding your camera close to your face and press the shutter button gently, so the camera doesn't shake.

TIP #2: CARRY YOUR CAMERA WITH YOU ALL THE TIME

Make it a habit to always carry your camera with you wherever you go. You never know when an opportunity for a great shot will occur. Be ready! You don't want to miss that once-in-a-lifetime moment.

▲ **Use the zoom feature on your camera to get in close for amazing shots!**

✔ Take your camera along wherever you go.

✔ Carry your camera in a case with a clip or belt loops to attach to your waist. You can also use a waist or "fanny" pack. These free your hands but keep your camera within easy reach when needed.

✔ Charge your camera battery each night or have extra batteries available so your camera always has sufficient power.

✔ Carry extra memory cards. You don't want to miss out on a great shot because your memory card is full.

TIP #3: TAKE LOTS OF PICTURES

▲ Try to include people in your photos along with landmarks. Here children enjoy the spray from a geyser in Yellowstone National Park.

One advantage of digital cameras is that you can take lots and lots of photos, and then choose the ones you like best and want to keep. Digital memory cards can hold hundreds of photos compared to the 24 or 36 shots on a traditional roll of film. Photos can be viewed almost instantly on the camera's display screen, allowing you to view pictures you've taken and delete the ones you don't like. This frees up space on the memory card for even more pictures!

✔ Take as many pictures as you can. Try different angles, zoom in, zoom out - experiment!

✔ Balance the types of photos you take. Try to take just as

many pictures of people as you do things and places.

✔ Use the camera's display screen to review the photos you just took. If you are not happy with the results, take additional pictures.

✔ Each night, review the photos you took that day. Delete ones you don't like to free up additional space on the memory card.

TIP #4: GET IN THE PICTURE

The photographer is often absent from vacation photos because they are behind the camera taking all the pictures! Use these tips to make sure you get into some of the family vacation photos.

▲ Check your camera's display screen after you take a shot. If you aren't happy with the picture, take another one.

✔ Pass the camera to someone else. Share the photography duties with other family members, such as a brother or sister. Take turns so everyone has a chance to be in some of the photos.

✔ Use your camera's self-timer to get into the photo yourself. Steady your camera on a solid object such as a table or rock, or use a tripod. Hit the self-timer and run around to get in front of the lens. Most self-timers will give you 10 to 15 seconds to get ready before the picture is taken.

▲ Capture candid moments from your trip when people are unaware you are taking their picture.

✔ Use more than one camera. If several members of your family carry a camera, everyone is sure to get into some of the photos.

TIP #5: TAKE CANDID SHOTS

Often vacation photographs look too posed with people standing in front of landmarks. Try capturing moments when people are not aware you are taking pictures. You'll get more relaxed, realistic photos that better depict your vacation experiences.

✔ Don't pose too many pictures. Rather than asking people to stop, turn, and smile for the camera, take candid pictures of them enjoying the moment.

✔ Try taking some silly photos. Catch people being goofy, but don't have them pose for the camera.

✔ When shooting landmarks, choose your point of interest and compose your photo in the viewfinder. Then catch your family "being themselves" in the foreground.

✔ Look for quiet moments to capture - mom and dad studying a map, your brother reading in the hotel, or your sister enjoying an ice cream at the park.

✔ Remember to have fun taking your vacation pictures. Don't over-think your photos - just shoot!

▲ **Place your subject off-center to create a more natural balance in your photos.**

Tip #6: Compose Your Shots

When you get ready to take a picture, take time to look through the viewfinder or LCD display. Take a close look to see what you are including and excluding in the photo. This is called composing the shot.

✔ Pick a point of interest, the visual focal point that is the main subject of your photo. This might be a person, such as a family member, or a thing, such as a statue or a mountain.

✔ Don't always place your subject in the center of the shot. Try shooting them off-center to the right or left for a more interesting perspective. This is sometimes called the "Rule of Thirds" because the best place to position the subject is along the outer third of the photo.

✔ Fill the rest of the frame with background which highlights where you are - a busy city street, a quiet mountain stream, or a colorful market.

▲ Zoom in close to fill the frame and capture people's facial expressions.

TIP #7: GET IN CLOSE

You'll get better photos if you zoom in close to your subjects. If you stand back too far, people and objects will look like tiny specks in the distance. Zooming in will allow you to capture details such as people's facial expressions. Fill the frame with only those things you want in the photo. Don't be afraid to use your feet to move closer to your subject or to get a shot from a different angle.

✔ Move in close or zoom in. Don't stand too far away. If possible, you should be within 6 feet of your subject.

✔ Back up to include more scenery. If you are including people in the picture, ask them to back up with you. Keeping them close will add depth to your photo.

✔ Include only as much of the background as is needed. Compose your shot. Is there something in the sky or the foreground you want to include?

✔ Take several photos of the same scene. Try different angles, perspectives, and settings.

TIP #8: CHANGE YOUR PERSPECTIVE

▲ Take pictures from a variety of angles to add interest to your photos.

Many amateur photographers take all their pictures from the same straight-on perspective. Try changing the angle from which you take a picture. Lay on the ground and shoot looking up at your subject, or stand on a chair to get a higher perspective. Don't take all horizontal pictures. Turn your camera to compose vertical shots.

✔ Experiment with different angles by looking through the viewfinder or LCD display before you take the picture.

✔ Move around. Crouch down, or stand on an object to get a picture looking down from above. Use your feet to look for creative shots!

✔ Don't back up to take pictures of tall subjects. Turn your camera to shoot vertically.

✔ Get down low and shoot vertically to compose very tall subjects (like a skyscraper).

✔ Try new things. Have fun while taking your photos!

TIP #9: BE AWARE OF BACKGROUNDS

When you compose your photos, be sure to study the entire frame, not just the subject you are shooting. Make sure there is nothing distracting in the background like a lamp post or tree limb that appears to be sticking out of someone's head.

▲ **Turn your camera vertically to take pictures of tall subjects.**

✔ Before you press the shutter button, take a moment to look at the background in the viewfinder. Does it complement your subject or is it distracting? Remember that all parts of the frame add up to make a photo.

✔ Zoom in or use your feet to move closer to your subject or use a different angle until the background is uncluttered.

✔ Use background to take interesting shots, such as a family member attempting to "hold up" a leaning building.

Tip #10: Check Your Lighting

Proper lighting can be the difference between a great shot and a poor one. Make sure you have enough light available, or use a flash. Many cameras have an automatic flash which goes on only when needed. But use your flash sparingly. Natural sunlight is best.

▲ **Make sure there is nothing distracting in the photo's background, like an errant tree limb or lamp post.**

✔ Keep the sun behind you or to the side. If the sun is behind your subject, it will cast a dark shadow over them.

✔ If you can't move so the sun is behind you, use your camera's flash to light your subject and minimize shadows.

✔ Keep taking pictures even if the sky turns gloomy or it starts to rain or snow. You can capture some dramatic shots during these less-than-ideal conditions.

✔ Try to avoid using a flash if possible. The flash on your camera will only light the area immediately in front of you, often resulting in poor pictures. Try shooting in low light without a flash. Use low lighting to be creative!

▲ Shooting in low light without a flash can often yield dramatic results.

TELLING A STORY WITH YOUR PHOTOS

Your pictures tell a story - the story of your vacation! Like all good stories, your vacation has a beginning, a middle, and an end. Make sure you cover all three in your photos. Rather than just taking a bunch of random pictures, think about how you want to "tell the story" of your vacation to your family and friends when you return home.

THE BEGINNING: START TAKING PHOTOS AT HOME

The beginning of your story includes all the planning and preparation as well as the travel to get to your destination.

Start taking pictures right away! Here are some ideas of things to shoot.

✔ Take pictures of family members packing bags for the trip.

✔ Capture your dad loading the car with luggage.

✔ Take a group photo of your family before you leave. Use your camera's self-timer or ask a friend to take the photo so you can be included.

▲ **Start taking pictures at the beginning of your trip - when you're packing the car, boarding the train, or waiting at the airport.**

✔ Get pictures of your family at the airport, boarding the train, taking the shuttle, or waiting for the bus to arrive.

✔ Shoot a close-up of your plane tickets or boarding passes.

✔ Photograph people who are part of your journey such as cab drivers, pilots, bus drivers, train conductors, and hotel staff. Catch them in action checking your bags, taking your tickets, etc.

THE MIDDLE: YOUR DESTINATION

Congratulations! You've reached your destination, as well as the middle of your story. This is the point where most people start taking pictures, but you're already deep into your photo journey. Keep documenting your travels with photos.

▲ **Shots from behind can show emotion, such as this photo at the Flight 93 National Memorial in Pennsylvania.**

✔ Take pictures of the places and landmarks you visit. Don't forget to include family members and others in some of your photos. Posed photos in front of landmarks are fine, but be sure to take some candid shots capturing people's expressions and their interactions at the location.

✔ Don't be afraid to shoot behind your subjects, capturing them looking up in awe at a snow-capped mountain or dancing to the rhythm of a street musician.

✔ Include photos along the way - in the car, on the road, at rest stops, etc.

✔ Take pictures of your hotel room, around the pool, and

at restaurants you visit.

✔ Use signs to introduce places. These serve as great chapter titles when creating a photo album or digital story. Take pictures of "Welcome to..." or "You are now entering..." signs. Photograph building marquees, historical plaques, street signs, and billboards. Have a family member hold a sign in front of a landmark.

▲ **Use signs to introduce new places and help tell your story.**

THE END: HEADING HOME

Like any good story, your photo journey needs an ending. Keep taking photos all the way to the end of your vacation. Record not only sights, but also people's actions and emotions as your trip comes to an end.

✔ Take photos of family members repacking and loading the car for the return trip home.

✔ Snap some final photos around your room. Capture your family leaving the hotel.

✔ Photograph the boat, plane, train, or bus you are traveling in.

✔ Take pictures of your family at the boarding gate or collecting luggage at the baggage carousel.

✔ Capture people's emotions. Catch them napping or playing games to pass time.

✔ Take photos at rest stops and restaurants on the way home.

✔ Capture a few final shots after arriving back home. Take pictures of people unpacking the car, greeting friends and neighbors, or reuniting with family pets.

▲ **Keep taking pictures at stops on the way home. Your vacation isn't finished yet!**

HAVE FUN WITH PHOTOGRAPHY

Above all, remember that these tips are suggestions, not rules you must follow. Don't worry if you cannot remember all these tips. You can always go back and review them occasionally to refresh your memory. Experiment and have fun with your photography!

WHAT'S NEXT?

Congratulations on completing your scavenger hunt around Washington, DC! You have uncovered clues, gathered points along the journey, and collected a well-deserved award. You have also kept a daily journal to record your travel memories and taken photos to document your adventure. Above all, you had a great time visiting Washington, DC!

When you return home, be sure to check out the free digital story tutorials on the Scavenger Guides website. These tutorials will teach you how to record your daily journal writings and combine them with digital pictures from your trip to create a multimedia travel video. This video is sure to become a treasured remembrance of your vacation for the entire family!

If you enjoyed this scavenger hunt around Washington, DC, check out our guides to other destinations. Visit http://www.scavengerguides.com to learn more.

Happy traveling!

▲ **Gap of Dunloe, County Kerry, Ireland.**

ABOUT THE AUTHOR

For as long as he can remember, Daniel Ireland has loved to travel. As a young boy, he traveled extensively throughout North America and Europe with his parents and three siblings. He now shares his passion for travel and adventure with his own family. When he's not on the road, he can be found in Grand Haven, Michigan, where he lives with his wife, Nancy, and their two children, Megan and Andrew.

Made in the USA
Lexington, KY
05 June 2011